W9-CFK-092

DAN FRONTIER, TRAPPER

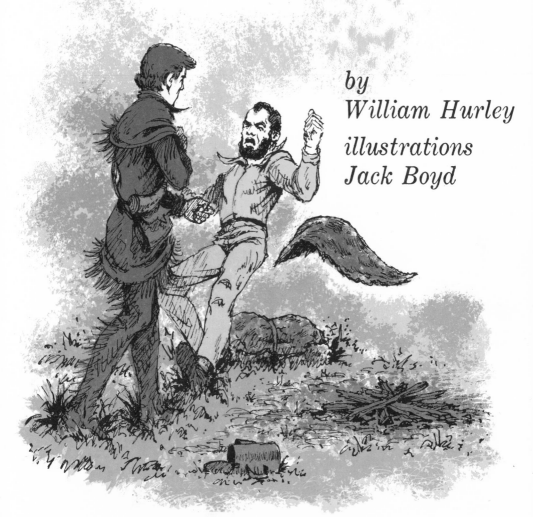

by
William Hurley

illustrations
Jack Boyd

BENEFIC PRESS • CHICAGO

PUBLISHING DIVISION OF BECKLEY-CARDY COMPANY

Atlanta   Long Beach   Dallas   Portland

DAN FRONTIER

DAN FRONTIER AND THE NEW HOUSE

DAN FRONTIER GOES HUNTING

DAN FRONTIER AND THE BIG CAT

DAN FRONTIER WITH THE INDIANS

DAN FRONTIER, TRAPPER

DAN FRONTIER SCOUTS WITH THE ARMY

DAN FRONTIER AND THE WAGON TRAIN

DAN FRONTIER, SHERIFF

DAN FRONTIER GOES EXPLORING

Library of Congress
Number 61-14670

STORIES

On the Way

Dan Frontier and Jimmy Healy were
riding away from Kettle Creek.

Dan and Jimmy were riding
to the trading post.

The trading post was a long way
from Kettle Creek.

"There are many furs
in the wagon," said Jimmy.
"We will get many things
for the furs," said Dan.

"Some are furs
of the Kettle
Creek people.
Some are my
furs," Dan said.
Jimmy asked,
"Where did you
get the furs?"

"We trapped beavers to get the furs," said Dan Frontier.

"Beavers have good furs."

"The Kettle Creek people are out of many things," said Dan.

"They want me to take the furs and get the things they must have."

Dan said, "I have some beaver
traps near here.

Soon we will stop to eat.

Then we will look at the traps.

There may be some beavers
in the traps."

Dan and Jimmy went on.

Then Dan said, "We will stop here to eat.

After eating, we will look at the traps."

Jimmy helped Dan get something
ready to eat.

After eating, Dan said, "The
traps are over by the river.

Come, we will look at the traps."

"Look here, Jimmy!" said Dan.

"Oh, Dan, that is a big beaver!"
Jimmy said.

Dan said, "This big beaver has a
good fur, too."

"Look down here
in these traps,
Dan!" called Jimmy.
"There are more
beavers down here."
Dan said, "I will
come here again
to trap beavers."

15

"We must get the furs ready
for the trading post," said Dan.

Dan and Jimmy worked and worked.

"Now these beaver furs are ready,"
Dan said.

"But how can you tell your furs
from the others?" asked Jimmy.

16

Dan said, "See this, Jimmy.
I put this on my beaver furs.
Something like this was put
on all the furs.
This is what your father put
on his furs."

"Now we must go," Dan said.
"I want to get these furs
to the trading post.
The Kettle Creek people want
you and me to get back soon."
Jimmy said, "They must have
the things from the trading post."

Robbers Come

Dan and Jimmy went on and on
with the wagon of furs.
Jimmy liked to ride with Dan.
He liked to hear Dan tell
about the ways of the Indians.

Jimmy said, "What Indians live
around here, Dan?"

Dan said, "Chief Black Fish
and his people live around here.

Black Fish has helped the people
of Kettle Creek in many ways.

They have helped his people, too."

Then Dan stopped his horse.
"Stop, Jimmy!" said Dan.
"Something is over there
in the woods.

I must see what it is.

I will call you when I want
you to come."

Little by little,
Dan went into
the woods.

Then he got down
near a tree and
looked all around.

"Jimmy!" called
Dan Frontier.

"I see a bear
over here.
He cannot
get away!"

"Then he must be in a trap,"
said Jimmy.

"What are you going to do?"

"I will have to get that bear
with my gun," said Dan.

"He may find a way to get out
of the trap.

Then he could come after you
and me."

Dan said, "I do not like to go after a bear this way.

But it is all I can do this time, Jimmy."

"Bang!" went Dan's gun.

The big bear went down.

"Come here, Jimmy," called Dan.

"The bear cannot get you now."

Dan and Jimmy looked at the bear.

"The people of Black Fish have traps like this one," said Dan.

"They must have put the trap here," Jimmy said.

Dan said, "Jimmy, will you look after the bear?

Look at the wagon and horses now and then, too.

I will ride over to the river."

"Black Fish's men
may be trapping in
the big river over
there," said Dan.

"I will tell his
men about the bear."

Jimmy called,
"Come back soon.

It will soon be
night, Dan."

Dan got on his horse, King,
and was on his way to the river.

After Dan went away, Jimmy looked
at the big bear.

He looked at the trap, too.

Then Jimmy sat down.

Soon Jimmy went to sleep.

"Get up, Jimmy!" called Dan.

"How can you look after things
when you are sleeping?

The men of Black Fish are here
with me."

Jimmy got up.

"I did not sleep long," he said.

"We put trap here for bear,"
one Indian said to Jimmy.

"You were good boy to sleep
near bear."

Jimmy said, "Dan wanted me
to look after things.

He did not want me to sleep."

Jimmy said, "I will not sleep again when you tell me to look after things."

"I know you will not do that again," said Dan.

"Come now, Jimmy.

It will soon be night.

We must make camp."

One of the Indians said, "We will take the bear back to Chief Black Fish.

We will tell Black Fish how you helped with the bear."

"Good-by, Friend Dan Frontier," said the Indians.

"Good-by, Friend Jimmy Healy."

"Good-by," said Dan and Jimmy.

Dan and Jimmy
went over to the
horses and wagon.
"Dan, Dan!"
called Jimmy.

"The furs are not
here!" Jimmy said.
"Oh, Jimmy!
When we were
away, robbers
came," said Dan.

"They must have come when you were sleeping," Dan said.

Jimmy wanted to cry.

"Oh, what can I do?" Jimmy said to Dan.

"What will the people do? We can not get the things they want from the trading post."

"This is not a time for crying,"
said Dan Frontier.

"We must get back the furs.

I will go over and tell the
Indians about this.

We must tell them to be on the
lookout for someone with many furs.

I will tell the Indians what
to look for on the furs."

"Jimmy, will you get all the
horses ready?" said Dan.

"We cannot take the wagon.
We have to go fast this time.
I will ask the Indians to take
the wagon.
Then we can get it back
from them sometime."

Dan went to see the Indians.

Jimmy got the horses ready.

When Dan Frontier came back,
Jimmy said, "The horses
are ready."

"Good," said Dan Frontier.

"Soon the Indians will be
ready to go.

Then they will come over
and get the wagon."

Over the Bridge

Away went Dan and Jimmy.

Dan said, "The fur robbers will
have to stop soon to make camp
for the night.

I do not know how many fur robbers
there were.

But I do know that one man could
not get away with that many furs."

"We must look all around
as we go along in these woods,"
said Dan.

"The robbers could jump out
and trap us."

"How do you know the robbers
went this way?" asked Jimmy.

Dan said, "They will be going
to the trading post with the furs."

"They will trade the furs
for things they want," Dan said.
"Then they will get away fast."
"Look, Dan," said Jimmy.
"We are near the river again."
"I see," said Dan.

Dan said, "The river is not too big here.

But it will get big soon."

Jimmy asked, "Do we have to cross the river?"

"Soon we will cross it," said Dan.

"The trading post is way over there."

Dan said, "Jimmy, I know a way
to trap the robbers!

Near here is a rope bridge.

The bridge was made by some
men of long ago.

Not many people know
about this bridge."

"The robbers will cross
with the boatman," Dan said.

"They will cross down where
the river is big.

We will go over the rope bridge
near here.

The robbers will not be looking
for us to cross here."

Jimmy said, "Then we can trap
them when they make camp."

"Come, Jimmy," said Dan.

"We will ride over to the bridge.

Ride near me, Jimmy.

It is night now, and your horse

may walk too near the river."

Jimmy said, "Look, Dan!
That must be the bridge."
"That is it," said Dan.
"Get down and walk now.
We will go across one
at a time."

"We will not take the wagon horses across," said Dan.

"We will take my horse.

I will put the wagon horses here near these trees.

No one can see them then.

We will come back for them."

Dan said to Jimmy, "Now, go on across, Jimmy.

Then I will come with King."

Jimmy walked to the bridge.

He did not like to look down.

Little by little, he got across the bridge.

Then Dan said to his horse,
"Come, King, we must go.
  Whoa-a-a-a, King, not too fast.
  Good boy, King.
  Whoa-a-a-a, King, whoa-a-a-a."
  "The bridge is moving!"
called Jimmy.

Dan and King stopped.

Then King jumped.

"Down, King!" called Dan Frontier.

"Dan, look out!" called Jimmy.

"The bridge is moving fast now."

"Down, King, down!" called Dan.
But King did not get down.
Dan pulled and pulled.
Down went King.
Down went Dan, too.

"Can I help you?" Jimmy
called to Dan.

"No, do not get on the bridge,"
called Dan.

Then Dan got up.

He said, "Come now, King."

This time King did not jump.

Little by little, Dan and King
got across the bridge.

"You made it!" said Jimmy.
"I made it," said Dan.
"But King did not like
that bridge."

"Now, Jimmy, you and I will
ride King," Dan said.

"He is a big horse and can hold
you and me."

"King is a fast horse, too,"
said Jimmy.

After the Robbers

Dan Frontier got on King.
Then he helped Jimmy get up.
"We will not go too fast now,"
said Dan.
"We cannot see some things
in the night."

On and on went Dan and Jimmy.

They looked and looked all
around as they went along.

Then Jimmy said, "When will
we stop to eat?"

Dan said, "I know you want
to eat.

But we cannot stop now.

We must trap the robbers
at night.

They cannot see us at night."

"Sh-h-h-h, Jimmy," said Dan.
"Whoa-a-a-a, King.
I see something up there."
"I see it, too," said Jimmy.
"It must be someone camping,"
Dan said.

Dan said, "We will get down now.

I will put King back here in the trees.

Then we will go as near as we can to the camp.

Here, King," said Dan.

"Good boy, sh-h-h-h."

Dan and Jimmy went as near as they could.

"I see a man over there," Dan said to Jimmy.

"Is he one of the fur robbers?"
asked Jimmy.

"I do not know, Jimmy," said Dan.

"We will look around and maybe
we can see something more.

Get down, and we will move over."

"Look, Dan!" said Jimmy.

"There are the furs of the
Kettle Creek people!"

"There is just one robber here,"
said Dan.

"But there must be more robbers.
We must take the furs and get
out of here fast."

"How are we going to do that?"
asked Jimmy.

"This is the way we will get
the robber and the furs,"
said Dan Frontier.

"You go over that way and move
around in the trees.

The robber will get up to look.

When he gets up to look your way,
I will jump him from over here."

"Are you ready, Jimmy?"

"Ready," said Jimmy.

Little by little, Jimmy moved over near some little trees.

Dan moved over the other way.

Jimmy jumped up and down.

The robber jumped up and got his gun.

Dan was just in time.

He jumped out and pulled down the robber.

Jimmy got the robber's gun.

"These are not your furs.

They are furs of the Kettle Creek people," said Dan.

"This is what we put on the furs," Dan said.

"We know that these are not your furs.

Now, come and help us get these furs out of here.

Do just what I tell you.

We will have a gun at your back all the time."

Dan Frontier made the robber work fast.
And Dan and Jimmy worked fast, too.
"Now, move along!" called Dan to
the robber.

"We will put these furs
on King's back.
Then we will come
back for the
other furs."

Soon there were many furs
on King's back.

Then Dan, Jimmy, and the
robber went back for more furs.

"Now we must get out of here
fast," Dan said.

Trapped

Jimmy got up on King.

Dan and the robber walked.

They moved as fast as they could.

As they went along, Dan asked the robber, "How many men helped you take the furs?

Where are the other men?"

But the robber just walked along.

Dan said to the robber, "We do not have time now.

But when we stop, I will make you talk."

On and on went Dan and Jimmy with the robber.

"Where are you taking me?" asked the robber.

"You will see," said Dan.

"There is the bridge!"
called Jimmy.

"We must get the furs across
as fast as we can," said Dan.

"The other robbers will soon
be after us."

"I will go over with King,"
Dan said.

"Jimmy, you must look
after this robber.

Have your gun ready."

Dan got some of the furs
from King's back.

"I know you cannot get all
of these furs across at one time,"
Dan said to King.

Dan and King went over
to the bridge.

"Be a good boy," Dan said.

Little by little, Dan and King
went across the bridge.

King jumped a little.

But Dan said, "Down, King.
Whoa-a-a-a, boy."

King stopped jumping.

Soon Dan and
King were across
the bridge.

Dan put King with
the other horses.

Then he went
back to Jimmy.

Dan said, "Now,
you take some
furs over."

"The robber will cross the
bridge after you do, Jimmy,"
Dan said.

"Have your gun ready
when you get over there."

Jimmy did not like crossing again.
But he did not tell this to Dan.

Jimmy did not go across
the bridge fast.

He was holding many furs.

The bridge moved a little,
but Jimmy did not stop.

Little by little, he went on.

"I made it!" Jimmy called.

Jimmy put down the furs.

He got ready for the robber.

Jimmy saw the robber coming over the bridge.

Soon the robber was across the rope bridge.

"Put the furs down here," Jimmy said to the robber.

"Now, do not move at all."

"I have the robber,"
called Jimmy to Dan.

"Then I will come over,"
called Dan Frontier.

Dan got out on the bridge.

Many, many furs were
on his back.

He could not move fast.

"Oh, I have too many furs
on my back," thought Dan.

Dan stopped on the bridge,
and then went on again.

"Dan, Dan!" called Jimmy.

"Look in back of you!"

Dan looked back over the bridge.

"Oh, the robbers!" thought Dan.

He wanted to move fast,
but he could not.

"Dan, come fast!" called Jimmy.

"Look what they are doing
to the bridge!"

"I cannot come fast," called Dan.

77

"What can I do?" thought Dan.
"I cannot hold on to these furs."
Down, down, down went the furs.
"Now I do not have the furs.
Maybe I can move fast," thought Dan.
"The bridge will not hold too long."

Just then, Jimmy called,
"Dan, someone is coming."
Dan looked around again.
"The men of Black Fish are
coming," Dan called to Jimmy.
"Come fast!" Dan called
to the Indians.

The robbers
looked up when
they saw the
Indians coming.

Then away went
the robbers.
But two Indians
went after them.

"Get to the
bridge!" Dan
called to the
other two Indians.
"The bridge is
going down.
I cannot hold
on too long."

The Indians got to the bridge
as fast as they could.

"Hold on!" called one Indian.

"We will hold on to ropes
over here.

Then bridge cannot fall."

"I cannot walk on the bridge
now," thought Dan.

"It is moving too fast.

I will have to cross the
bridge this way.

It is all I can do now."

"Help, help!" called Dan.
"The bridge is going down!"
One of the Indians called,
"Hold on, hold on!"

"We could not hold ropes,"
called one Indian.
"Ropes got away from us.
But we have ropes now.
Bridge will not fall."
The bridge was moving fast.
Dan said, "Oh, I must make it."

"You will soon make it, Dan,"
called Jimmy.

"Come just a little more.

Good for you!

You made it!"

"Oh, Jimmy, it is good to be
here," said Dan.

"I thought I was going to be
way down there."

"I see the robber did not get away from you," said Dan.

"You were a big help, Jimmy."

"Look, Dan," said Jimmy.

"The other two Indians have come back with the robbers."

"Men of Black Fish," called Dan Frontier.

"You have helped us again. You have trapped the robbers."

Dan called to the Indians,
"We will get the furs and the
horses ready now.

You go down the river to where
the boatman stops.

We will cross the river
with the boatman.

We will see you where the
boatman stops."

Then Dan got the horses and
the furs ready.

He got the robber ready, too.

Soon they were on the way.

"It is good to have the horses
again," said Jimmy.

"They are a big help
with all these furs."

"I see the sun coming up,"
said Jimmy.

"And I see the boatman down
there," said Dan.

"Come, King," said Dan.

"We must get across the river.
The Indians will be looking
for us."

Soon they stopped
the horses near
the river.

Dan helped the
boatman get the
horses onto the
big boat.

Then they were
on their way
across the river.

"I see the
Indians over there,"
said Dan Frontier
to Jimmy.

"Here we are!" called Jimmy,
as the boat stopped.

"And it is good to see you,"
said one Indian.

"Here are the robbers," said
one of the Indians.

"Men of Black Fish, you have
helped us again," said Dan.

"I will tell the people of
Kettle Creek how you helped us."

"And I will tell the people
how you crossed that bridge,"
said Jimmy to Dan.

"I will tell how we got the
furs away from the robbers, too."

"We all helped," Dan said.

"And now we can go on
to the trading post with the furs.

The people back in Kettle Creek
will get the things they want."

VOCABULARY

The total vocabulary of this book is 142 words. Of these, 22 are first-grade words; 11 are above first grade; and the rest are below. First-grade words are listed in roman type, and those above are in italics. The words are listed in alphabetical order, and the numbers indicate the pages on which the words first appear.

as 38

bear 22
beavers 9
boatman 42
bridge 37

camp 30
cross 40
cry 33

furs 7

gun 23

hold 52

horse 21

Indians 19

just 59

long 6

many 7
men 26
more 15
moving 47

near 11

others 16

people 18
post 6
pulled 49

river 13
robbers 19
rope 41

these 15
thought 76
trading 6
trapped 9

wagon 7
woods 21

DEVELOPMENT OF READING SKILLS

Reading is an important skill integral in learning any subject area. The prerequisite for effective use of reading material is interest. If the child has genuine interest in content, the exercise of reading skills becomes meaningful and enables him to transfer these skills to basic books in any subject.

The supplementary reader provides, in a high-interest story, the exercise and development of reading skills learned in the basic reader.

THE READING SKILLS

I Promoting Growth in Interpretative Skills

Interpreting the main idea

The high-interest and fast-moving plot of this book is built around a trip that Dan Frontier and Jimmy Healy make from Kettle Creek to the trading post with a wagon of furs. Crossing a perilous swinging bridge and chasing fur robbers are a part of the excitement encountered by Dan and Jimmy on this trip. The main theme can be easily followed by reading pp. 5-7, 10, 18, 32-34, 41-42, 54, 59, 62, 66, 68, 86-87, 92-93.

Comprehending phrase and sentence meanings

Clear narrative writing helps the reader to understand fully a situation, a scene of action, or a characterization. Note narration on pp. 27, 71, 73, and 91. With the narration and the pictures the reader can easily envision the activity. *6, 22, 61.

Observing details and understanding their relationship

A plot is strengthened if significant details relative to the main idea are written into the story at strategic points. Note the importance of the details on p. 60 where Jimmy and Dan are planning their strategy. These details make it possible for the reader to understand just exactly how Dan and Jimmy trapped the fur robber.

Interpreting a story in sequence

A chain of logically planned events in a story shows the child how certain happenings result in a related action. On pp. 7-10, the reader finds out why Dan and Jimmy are taking the furs to the trading post. On p. 32, the reader learns that the furs are stolen, and this logically leads to a decision by Dan on p. 34 to go after the robbers. The chase ends with the recapture of the furs on p. 63 and the capture of the robbers on p. 87.

Making inferences

Children will learn to read more intelligently and with more enjoyment if they are given an opportunity to make inferences. On p. 42, Dan tells Jimmy that they will cross the river on a little known rope bridge. The reader can infer that this decision is going to give Dan the advantage over the fur robbers.

Forming associations

A well planned story with meaningful details, descriptions, and pictures helps the reader to form the proper associations. After reading pp. 20, 26, 29, 31, 34-35, 87, and 92, the readers will very easily associate the good qualities of friendliness, helpfulness, trustworthiness, and sincereness with Chief Black Fish's men.

Forming sensory images

To be able to feel or visualize experiences of the story characters is a necessity if a reader is going to find real meaning and interest in his reading. On p. 34, the child will, no doubt, experience the sadness that Jimmy feels. *48-49, 51, 76-79, 82-86.

Anticipating outcomes

By taking note of important details and anticipating outcomes, a child finds his reading much more challenging. For example, after reading p. 34, the child will anticipate that the Indians will probably appear again sometime later in the story to help Dan and Jimmy in the pursuit of the fur robbers.

Making judgments and drawing conclusions

If a child is comprehending what he is reading and is relating the pictures to the reading matter, he will be able to make intelligent judgments and conclusions. On pp. 23-24, the reader will conclude that Dan is a wise and experienced hunter. He had to shoot the bear because a wounded bear when free is a threat to man's life.

Strengthening memory by observation, association, and visual imagery

The child must remember certain descriptions and details relative to the main theme of the story in order to follow the plot intelligently. Note how the following pages emphasize that Dan is a wise and brave frontiersman: pp. 10, 17, 23-24, 38. *41-42, and 60.

II Promoting Growth in Word-Perception Skills

Establishing habits of viewing words in left to right serial order

The left-to-right movement is a basic skill in reading. By studying words that begin with the same initial blend but end differently and words that begin and end with the same letter but use a different middle letter, the child can increase both his reading skill and his skill in word identification. Note "trading" on p. 6 and "trapped" on p. 9, and "for" on p. 34 and "fur" on p. 37. *17 and 19.

Observing individual words or phrases in context

Recognition of words and phrases and the understanding of their meaning in relation to contextual material is of primary importance in gaining skill in reading. Note the use of the word "trap" on p. 23 in relation to beavers and again on p. 42 in relation to the fur robbers.

95

Strengthening memory of word forms based on association of meaning with printed words, careful observation of visual details, and visual imagery of words
Through association with the text and art work on pp. 44 and 46-50, the reader will have little difficulty in later identifying the word "bridge."

Using meaningful clues as an aid in identifying words
A good story should include meaningful clues to help the reader in identifying new words. The word "beavers" introduced on p. 9 is repeated on p. 11 and again on pp. 14 and 15 where there are good picture clues.

Developing phonetic skills, auditory perception of rhyme, visual auditory perception of rhyme, auditory perception of initial consonant sounds, substitution of initial consonants and auditory imagery
Use phonetic helps to further develop the reader's ability to hear a word and to sound out a word. Note the word "near" on p. 11 and the word "hear" on p. 19. Also, note the word "some" on p. 11 and the word "come" on p. 13. Also, notice the difference in the sound of the letter "e" in the word "bear" on p. 22 and the word "hear" on p. 19.

Developing structural analysis skills . . . recognition of words formed by adding "s" to known root words and recognition of compound words made up of two known root words
A vocabulary can be increased in several ways. Among these are learning to add "s" to known root words and learning the compound forms of known words. There are many examples in this story of words with and without the "s": "fur" and "furs"; "trap" and "traps"; "beaver" and "beavers"; and "Indian" and "Indians." The words "some" and "thing" appear in the story and later "something" appears.

Identifying words in capitalized and uncapitalized initial-letter forms
Give the children practice in identifying initial letters as they appear in capital and lower-case forms. This will permit them to begin sentences with more ease. Note the word "beavers" in its upper- and lower-case forms on p. 9; "After" on p. 12; and "after" on p. 23. *25 and 28.

Testing mastery of sight vocabulary
Children may be overly dependent on contextual clues for identification of words. Additional practice with words out of context may aid the child in mastering an enriched sight vocabulary. Go back over words of similar construction, such as "near" p. 11, "hear" p. 19, and "bear" p. 22; "trading" p. 6, and "trapped" p. 9.

III Promoting Growth in Language
Understanding that a sentence is a meaning unit
The way in which a particular word or group of words is used in a sentence determines the over-all meaning of the sentence. The same word or group of words might be used differently in another sentence. On p. 15, the word "trap" is used in connection with "beaver" and on p. 23, in connection with a bear; but on p. 38, the word "trap" is used in connection with people.

Enriching oral vocabulary
After reading the story, the child should have a broader knowledge of word meanings, and this will help him with his oral vocabulary. For example, the children probably did not think of a rope bridge as a means of crossing a river.

* Additional material which will help in developing this reading skill through story material may be found on the following pages: